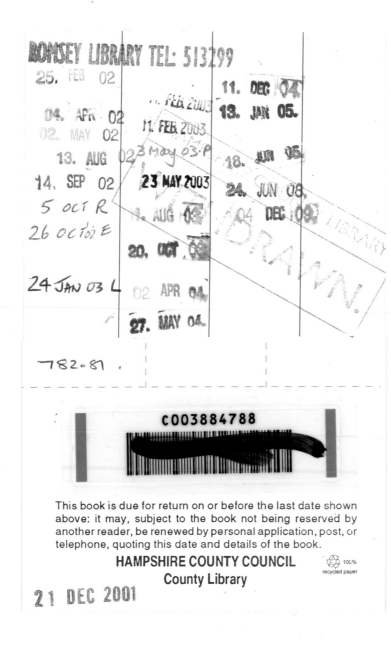

BRIDGET JONES'S DIARY

Music From The Motion Picture
for Piano, Vocal and Guitar

PUBLISHED 2001

© International Music Publications Ltd
Griffin House 161 Hammersmith Road London W6 8BS England

Production Anna Joyce
Folio Design Dominic Brookman
Cover Design green ink
With special thanks to Mercury Records and Elite Music
www.bridgetjonesdiary@msn.co.uk
Motion Picture based on the book by Helen Fielding,
published by PICADOR

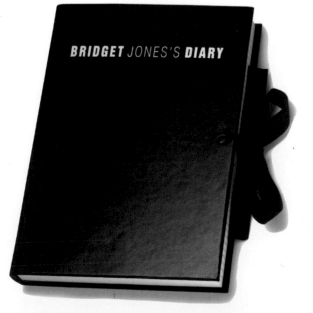

BRIDGET JONES'S DIARY

2001   **June**

Sunday   **10**
161-204   Week 23
Trinity Sunday

8 am

9   *Compilation album suitable for all occasions -* ①
     (especially most important romantic situations.)

10   *Top Artists included -* ⑭
     (including 1 x snoggable, 1 x v.thin and many -
     singing type gods & goddesses)

11

12 noon   *Songs which completely identify with -* ⑤

1 pm

2

2001   **June**

Monday   **11**
162-203   Week 24
Queen's Birthday Holiday (Australia)

8 am

9   *Songs which distract me and make me think of food -* ⑥
     (v.v.Good indeed)

10   *Songs which remind me never become a smug married -* ②

11   *Songs which do not completely understand -* ①
     (but sure writer/composer did at the time)

12 noon   *Positive thoughts whilst listening to soundtrack - Lots (v.v.Good)*

1 pm

2

BRIDGET JONES'S DIARY

Out Of Reach

Words and Music by Gabrielle and Jonathan Shorten

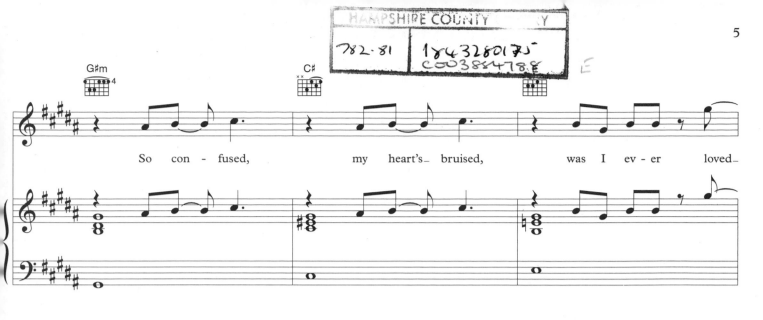

So con-fused, my heart's bruised, was I ev-er loved

by you. Out of reach. So far I nev-er had your heart.

Out of reach. Could-n't see we were nev-

er meant to be. 2. Catch my-self So much hurt,

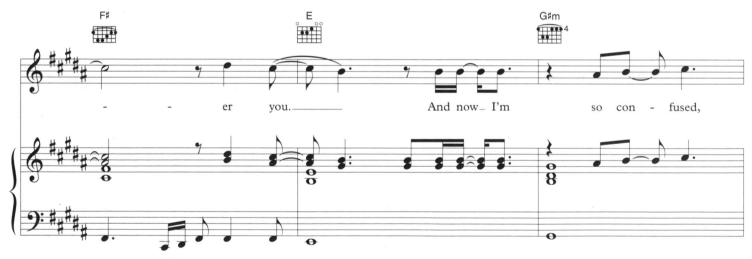

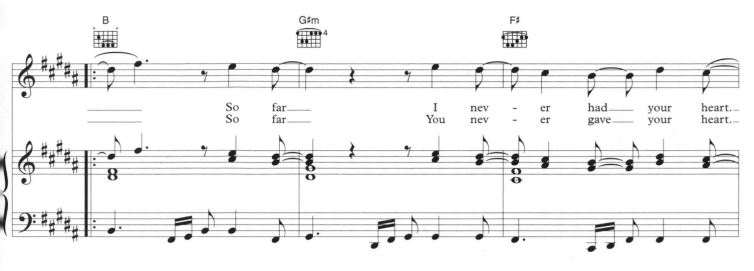

So far_____ I nev - er had_____ your heart.
So far_____ You nev - er gave_____ your heart.

Out of reach._____ Could-n't see_____ we were nev-
In my reach._____ I can see_____ there's a life

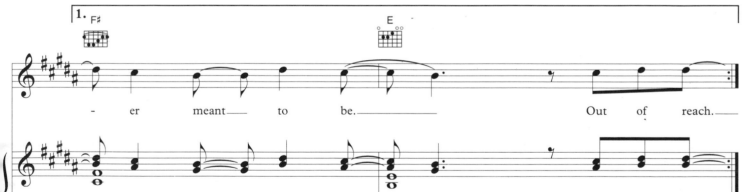

1. F♯

- er meant_____ to be._____ Out of reach._____

2. F♯

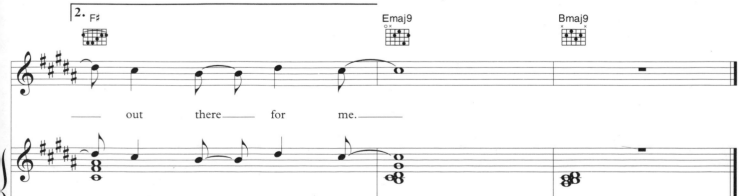

_____ out there_____ for me._____

It's Raining Men

Words and Music by Paul Jabara and Paul Shaffer

Hi, we're your Weather Girls. And have we got news for you. You'd better listen!

Get ready all you lonely girls. And leave those umbrellas at home.

-ing wet.___ It's rain-ing men.___ Hal-le-lu-

-jah. It's rain-ing men. Ev-'ry spe-ci-men. Tall, blonde,

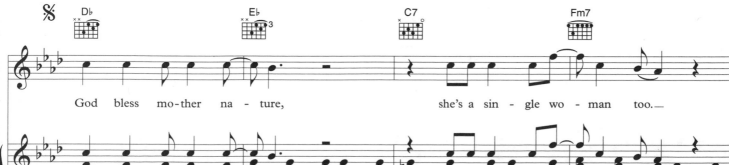

dark, lean. Rough and tough___ and strong___ and mean.___

God bless mo-ther na-ture, she's a sin-gle wo-man too.___

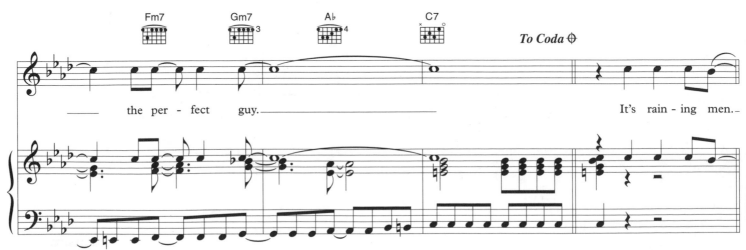

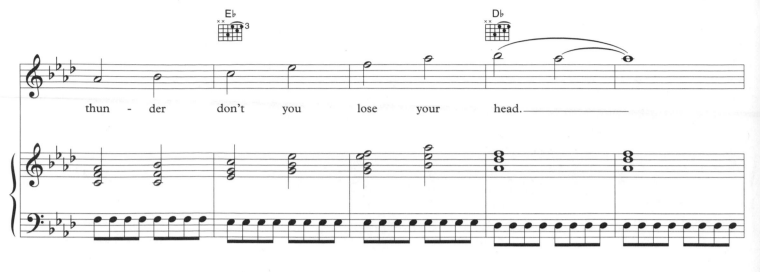

thun - der don't you lose your head.

Rip off the roof— and stay—— in bed.— Oh!

D.%. al Coda

⊕ *Coda*

Oh, ooh it's rain - ing men. Yeah!! Hu -

Play 3 times

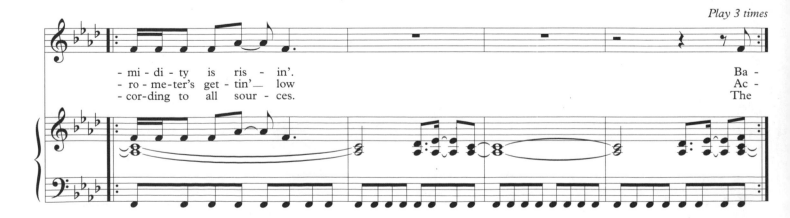

- mi - di - ty is ris - in'.   Ba -
- ro - me-ter's get - tin'— low   Ac -
- cor-ding to all sour - ces.   The

street's the place to go.___ 'Cos to-night for the first___ time,

just a-bout half past ten. For the first time in his - to - ry,___ it's

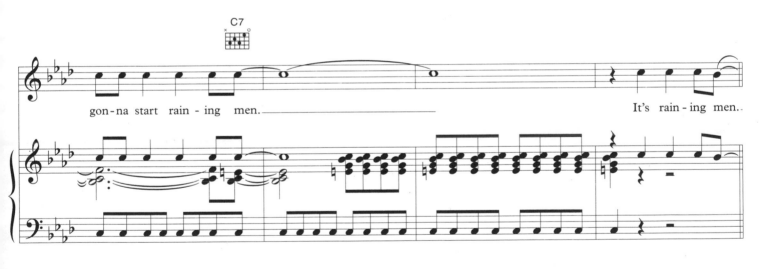

gon-na start rain - ing men._____ It's rain - ing men.

Repeat to fade

_____ Hal-le-lu - jah. It's rain - ing men. A - men. It's rain - ing men.___

Have You Met Miss Jones?

Words by Lorenz Hart
Music by Richard Rodgers

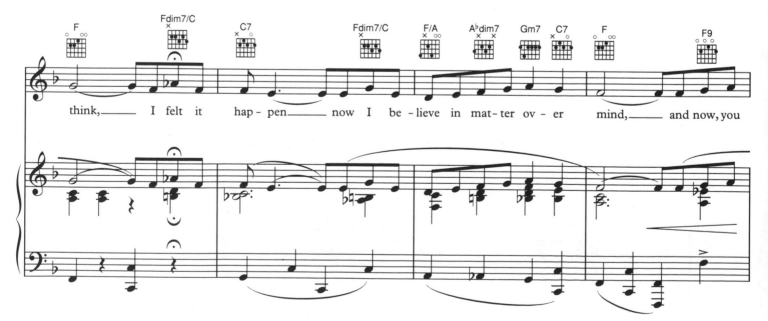

Respect

Words and Music by Otis Redding

What you want ba-by I got.
I ain't gon-na do you wrong while you gone.

What you need you know I got it.
I ain't gon-na do you wrong 'cause I don't wan-na.

All I ask-in' is for a lit-tle re-spect, when you come home. Ba-

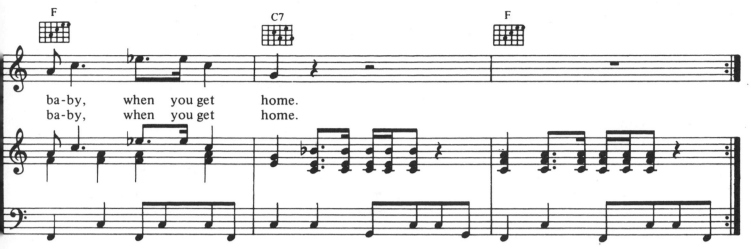

baby, when you get home.
baby, when you get home.

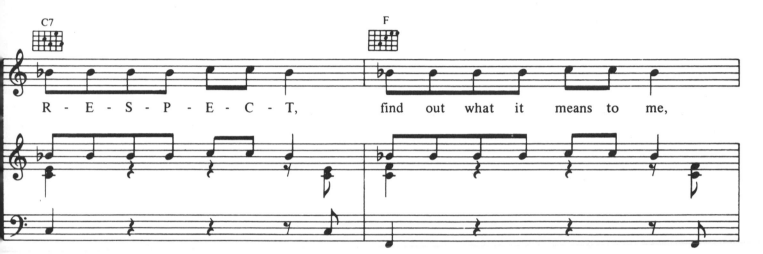

R - E - S - P - E - C - T,   find out what it means to me,

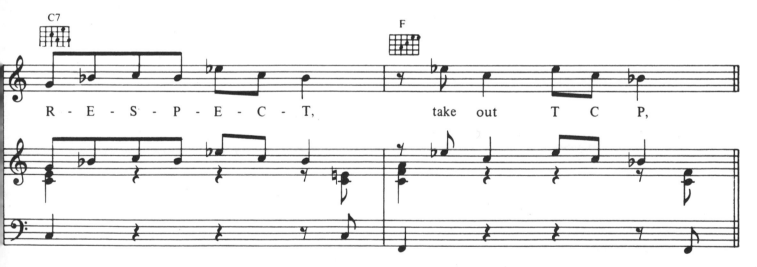

R - E - S - P - E - C - T,   take out T C P,

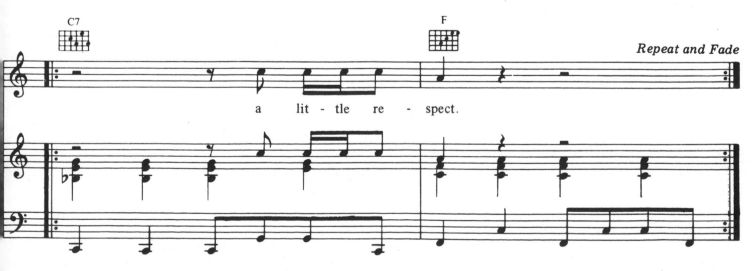

Repeat and Fade

a lit - tle re - spect.

I'm Every Woman

Words and Music by Nickolas Ashford and Valerie Simpson

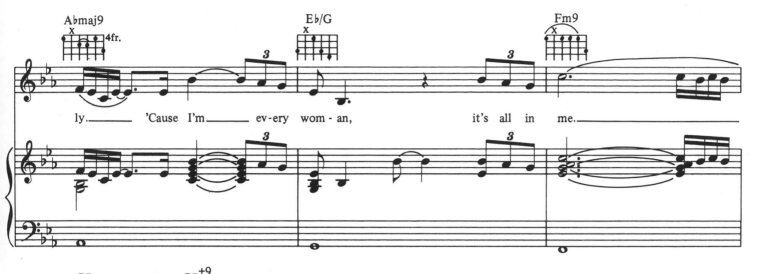

ly.____ 'Cause I'm____ ev-ery wom-an, it's all in me.____

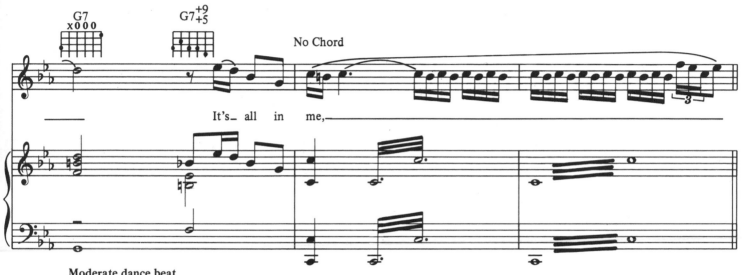

____ It's_ all in me,____

Moderate dance beat

yeah!

Additional Lyrics

2. I can sense your needs like rain unto the seeds.
I can make a rhyme of confusion in your mind.
And when it comes down to some good old-fashioned love,
I've got it, I've got it, I've got it, got it, baby, 'cause...
(To Chorus)

Don't Get Me Wrong

Words and Music by Chrissie Hynde

Swing semiquavers ($\quarternote = 102$)

1. Don't get me_ wrong, if I'm look-ing kind of daz-zled.

I see ne-on lights when-ev-er you walk

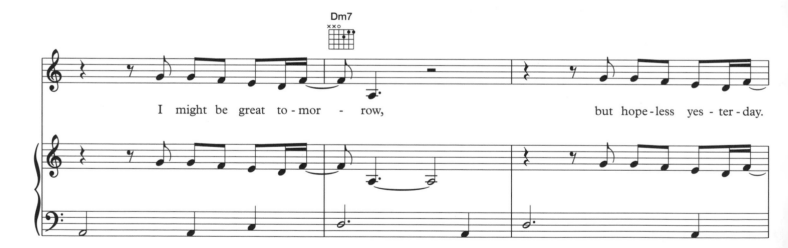

3. Don't get me___ wrong,_____ if I come and go like fash-ion.

I might be great to-mor - row, but hope-less yes-ter-day.

Don't get me___ wrong,_____

Kiss That Girl

Words and Music by Sheryl Crow

1. I woke up this morn - ing with my make - up on.
2. You're so glad you made it in this dead end town.

I been fak-ing it late - ly, but those days are gone.
Ev-'ery-bo-dy's wait - ing for you to come down.

You look at me and won - der why,_____ I got - ta cut these strings
You're gon - na wake up from_____ your dream,_____ you're gon - na find some - one_____

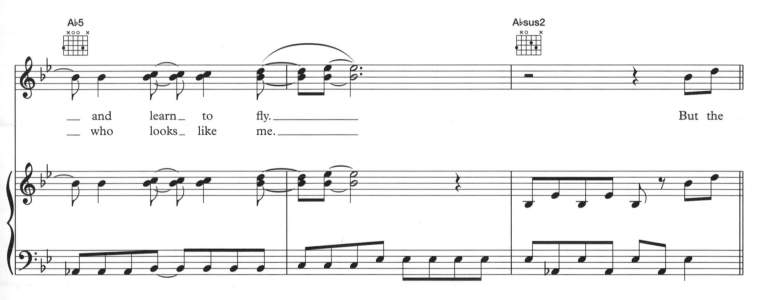

_____ and learn_ to fly._____ But the
_____ who looks_ like me._____

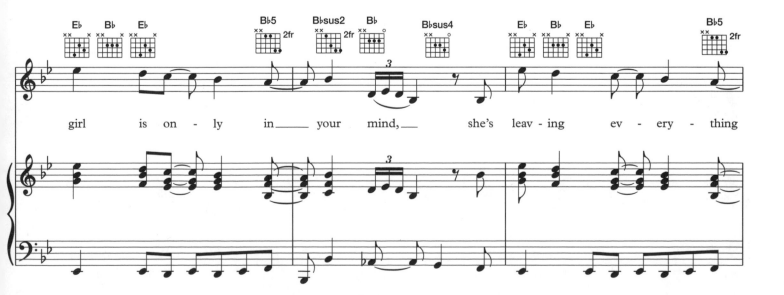

girl is on - ly in_____ your mind,_____ she's leav - ing ev - ery - thing

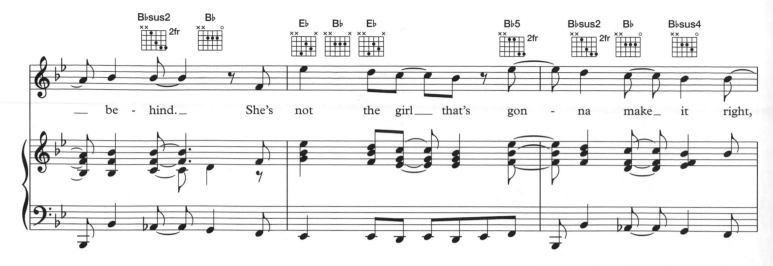

_ be - hind. _ She's not the girl_ that's gon - na make_ it right,

_ sure, you can kiss that girl_ good - bye. _

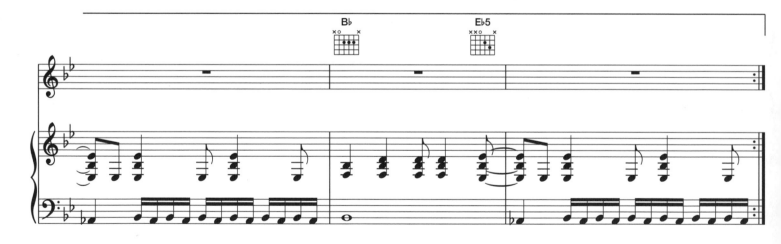

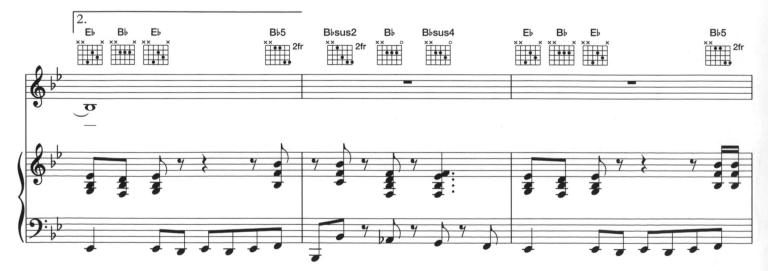

Killin' Kind

Words and Music by Shelby Lynne

Page 43

Chords: A, C#m7, Dmaj7, Bm7, E

-lin' kind,_____ oh yeah._

F#m, B7, F#m, B7

(Cry!) I just might cry_ now, (Lie!) lay down and die_ now.

F#m, B7

(Why!) You've done it to_ me, you're put-ting me un-der._____

A, C#m7, Dmaj7, Bm7, E

I close my eyes____ and I____ sit un-der____ the sky,_ I love you and all its plea-

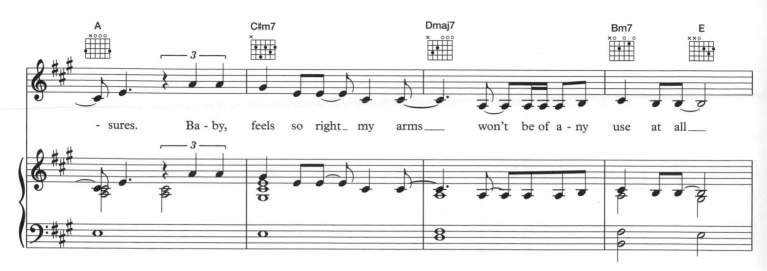

- sures. Ba - by, feels so right_ my arms__ won't be of a - ny use at all__

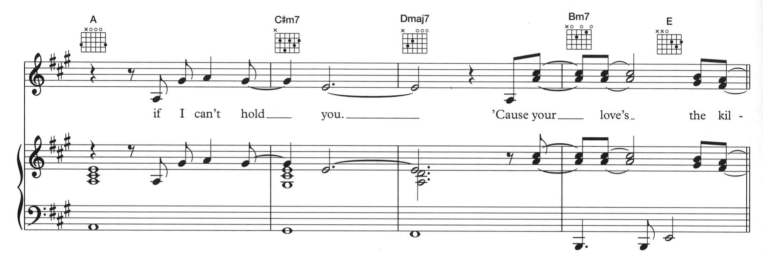

if I can't hold____ you._____ 'Cause your____ love's_ the kil -

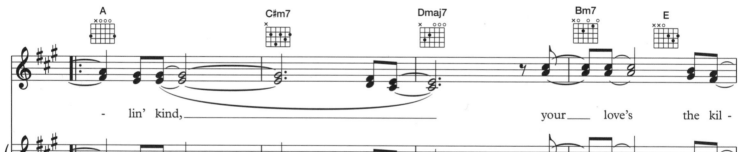

- lin' kind,_____ your____ love's the kil -

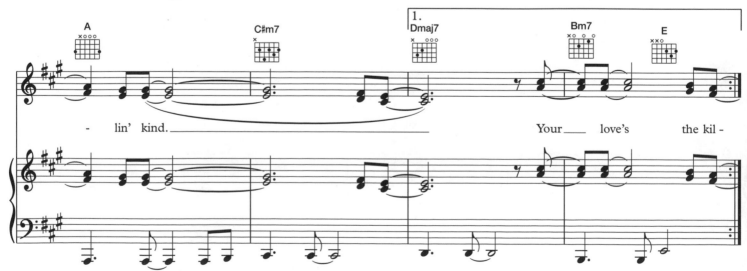

- lin' kind._____ Your____ love's the kil -

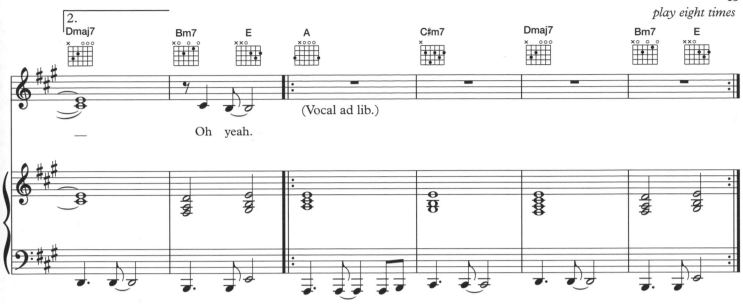

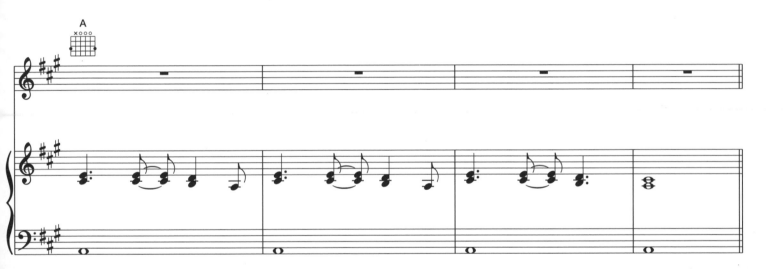

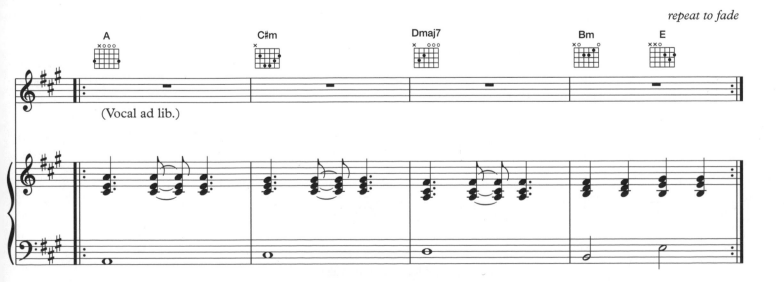

Someone Like You

Words and Music by Van Morrison

CODA

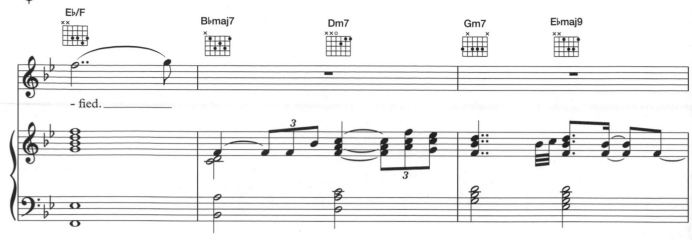

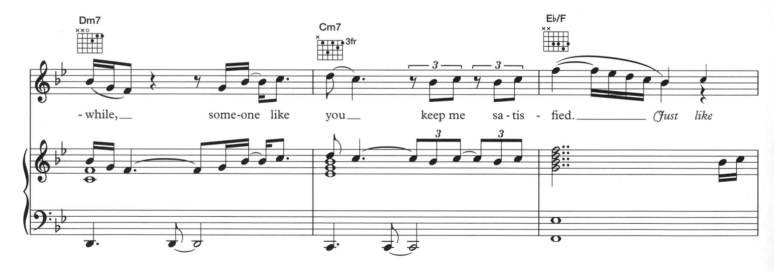

Not Of This Earth

Words and Music by
Robbie Williams and Guy Chambers

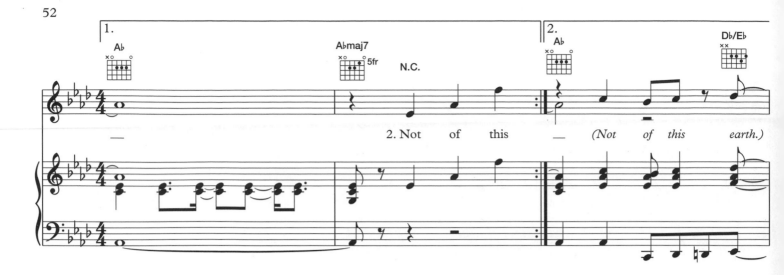

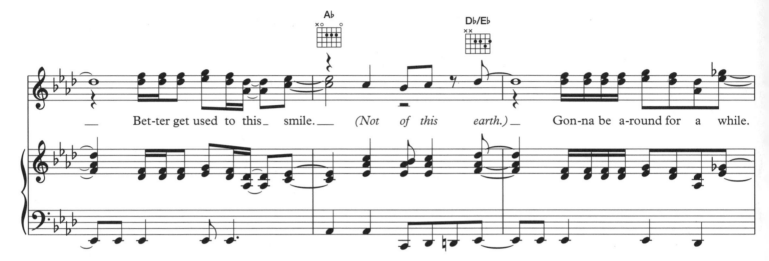

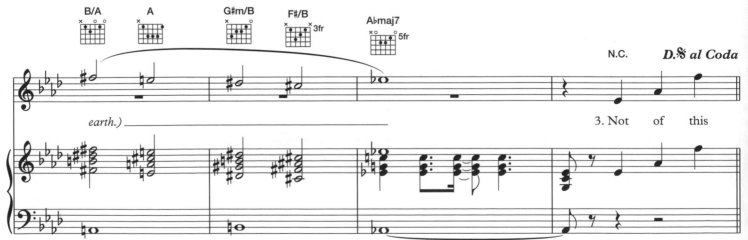

⊕ CODA

_(Not of this earth, ___ not of this earth, ___

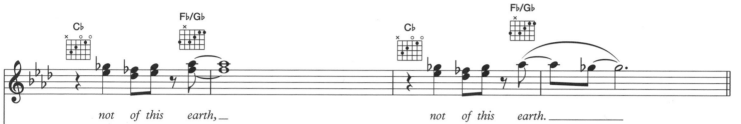

not of this earth, ___ not of this earth. _____

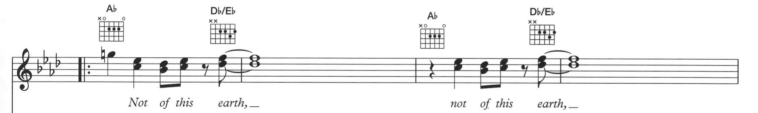

_Not of this earth, ___ not of this earth, ___

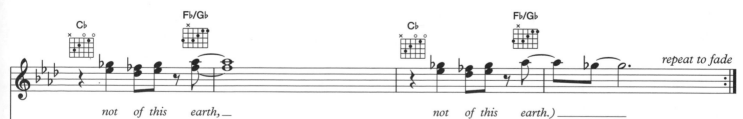

not of this earth, ___ not of this earth.) _____

repeat to fade

Can't Take My Eyes Off You

Moderate tempo

Words and Music by Bob Crewe and Bob Gaudio

You're just too good to be true, can't take my eyes off of you

way that I stare, there's noth-ing else to com-pare,

You'd be like heav-en to touch, I wan-na

the sight of you leaves me weak, there are no

hold you so much, at long last love has ar-rived, and I thank
words left to speak, but if you feel like I feel, please let me

God I'm a-live.
know that it's real.
You're just too good to be true, can't take my

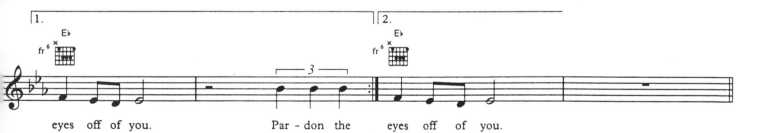

1.
eyes off of you.
Par-don the
2.
eyes off of you.

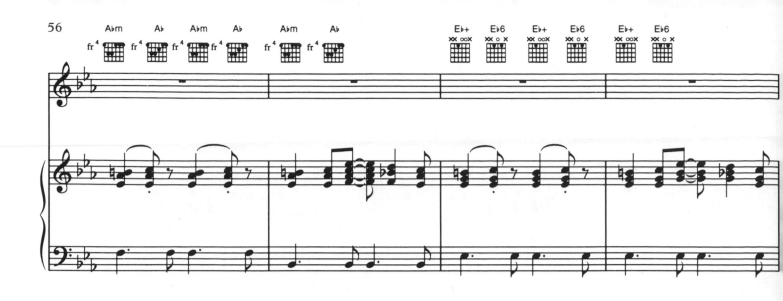

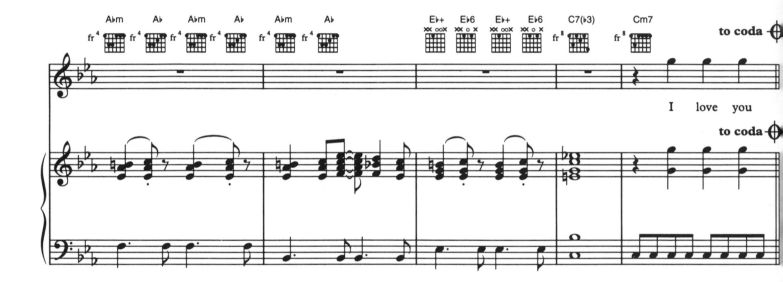

to coda ⊕

I love you

to coda ⊕

ba - by,___ and if it's quite all right,___ I need you, ba - by,___ to warm the

lone - ly night, I love you, ba - by,— trust in me—when I—— say:

Oh pret - ty ba - - by,— don't bring me down, I pray,— oh pret - ty

ba - - by—— now that I've found you, stay,— and let me love you,— ba -

- by, let me love you._____ You're just too

D. S. al coda ◇

Coda

ba - by,__ and if it's quite all right, I need you, ba - by,__ to warm the lone-ly night, I love you,

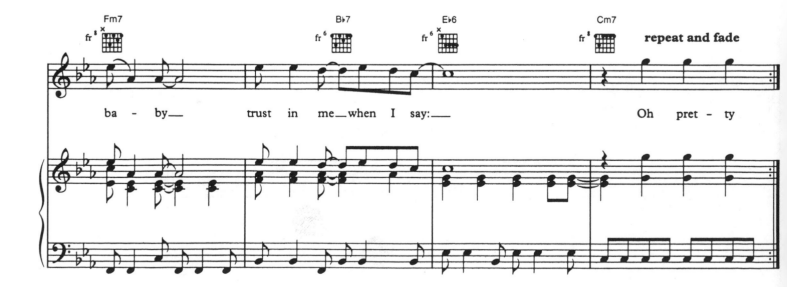

ba - by__ trust in me__ when I say:__ Oh pret-ty

Love

Words and Music by
Rosey and Darryl Swann

-fore. *Love, I am so dif - fer - ent,___* *love, I am so*

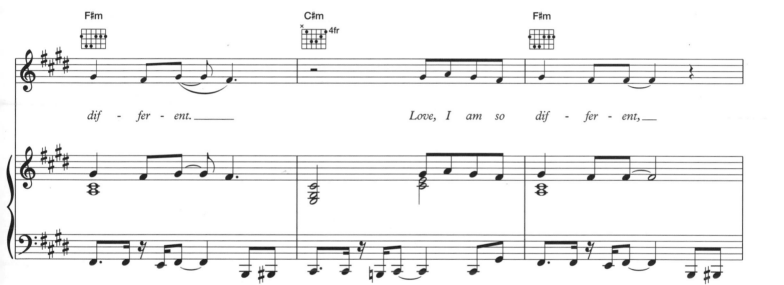

dif - fer - ent._____ *Love, I am so dif - fer - ent,___*

love, I am so dif - fer - ent._____

Dreamsome

Words and Music by
Shelby Lynne, Dorothy Overstreet and Jay Joyce

1. In the dark   I can hear   you whis - per. _
2. Make it mine,   tak-en time,   for - got - ten. _
3. Turned a - way, blu-er shade, when the sun comes.

Sha-dows still   move a - cross   the dis - tance.
Speak for me   si - lent - ly   sur - ren - der.
peace-ful time, cease your mind, and dream-some.

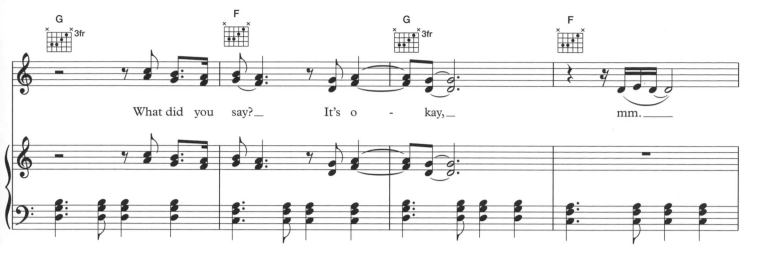

What did you say?__ It's o - kay,__ mm.____

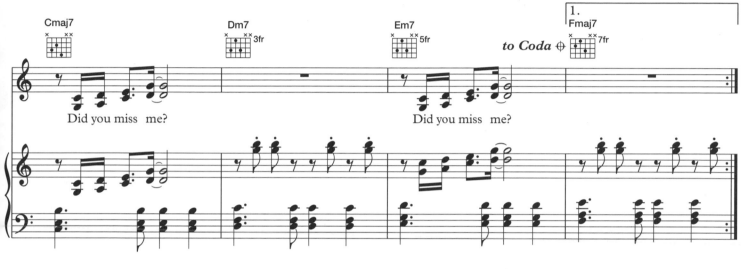

Did you miss me? Did you miss me?

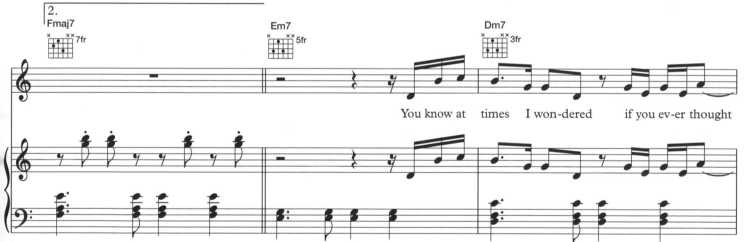

You know at times I won-dered if you ev-er thought

__ of me, and I won-dered if you want-ed to be free____ like me,__ and I

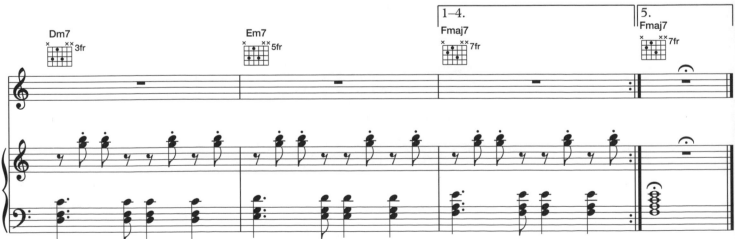

Stop, Look, Listen (To Your Heart)

Words and Music by
Thom Bell and Linda Creed

70

All By Myself

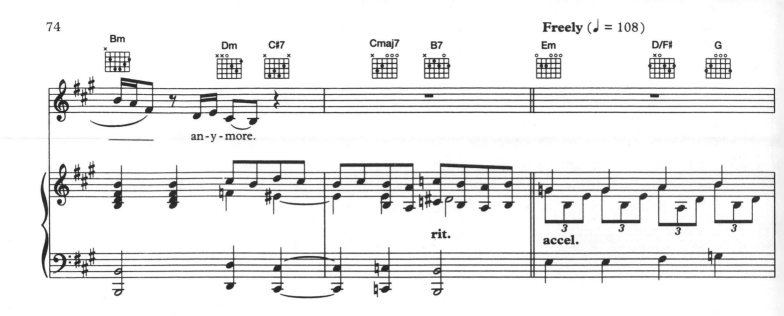

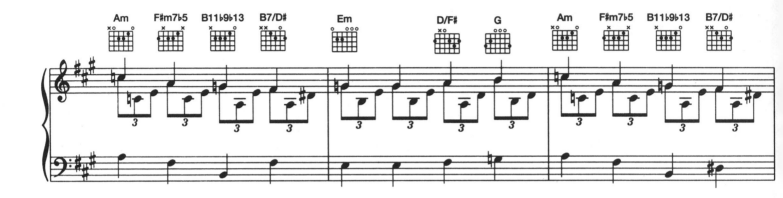

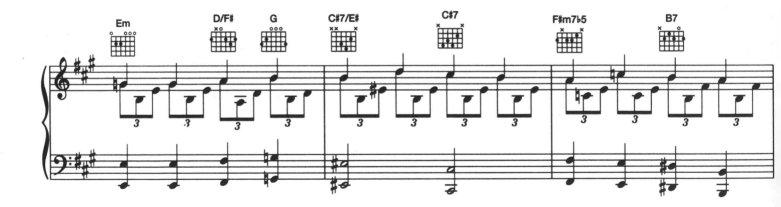

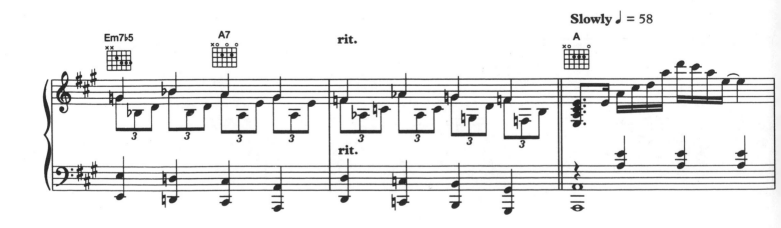

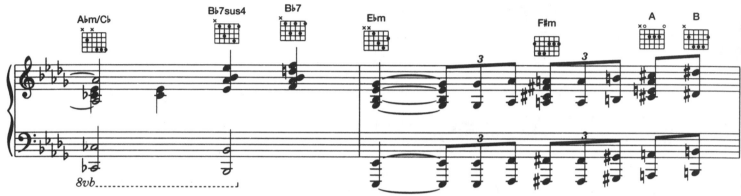

All by____ my - self,_____ don't wan - na live,

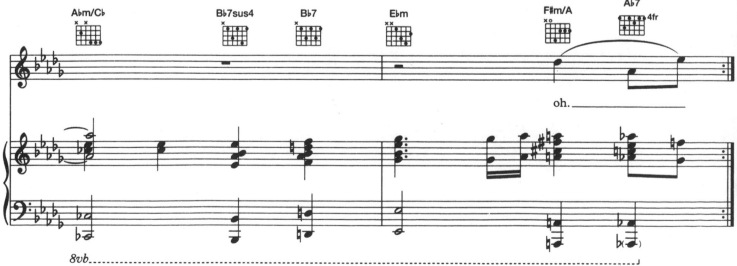

repeat ad lib. and fade

oh. _____

It's Only A Diary

Music by Patrick Doyle

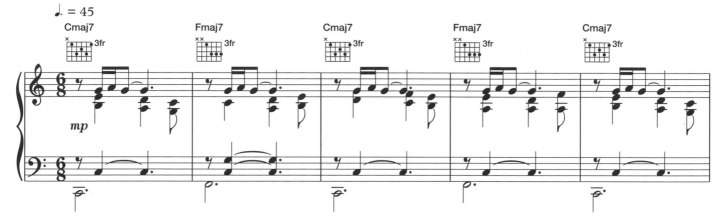

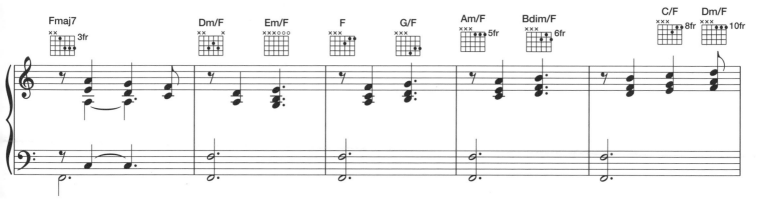

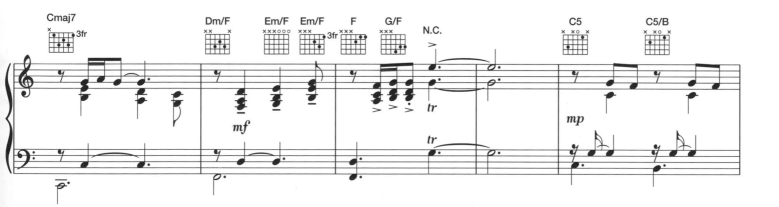

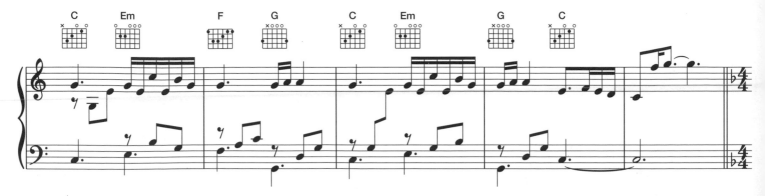

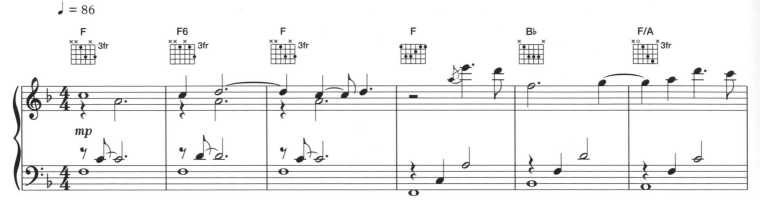

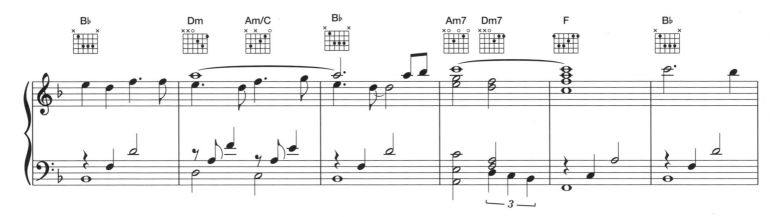

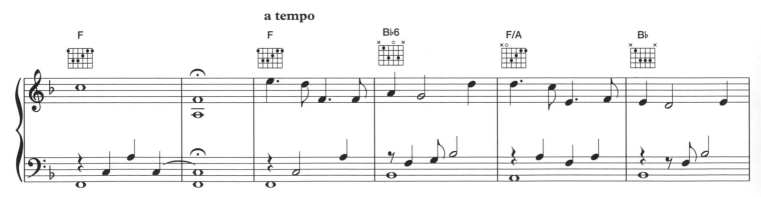

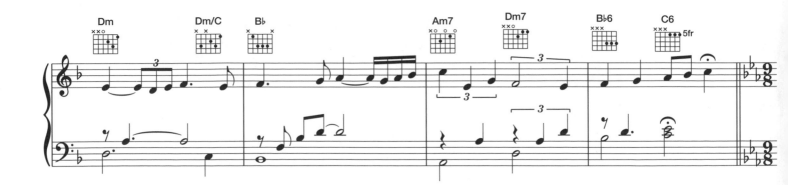

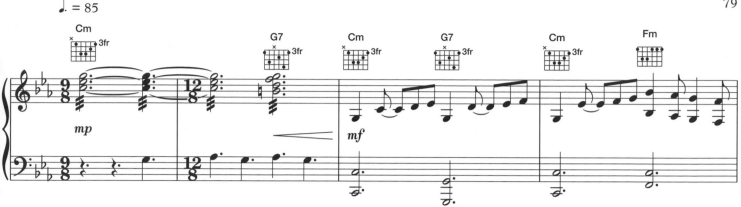

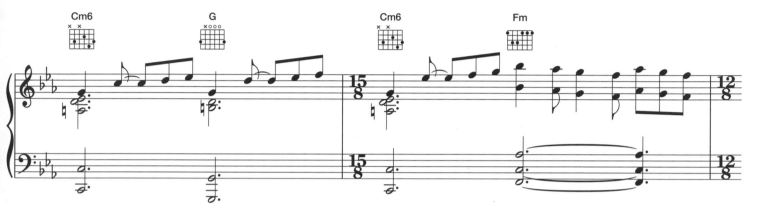

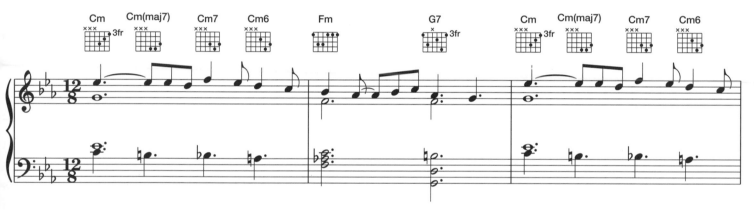

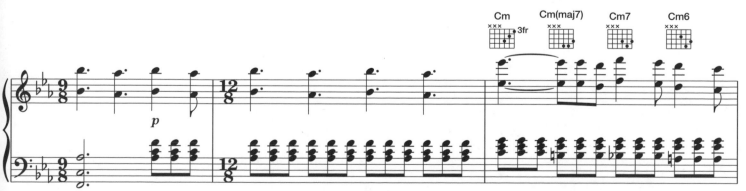

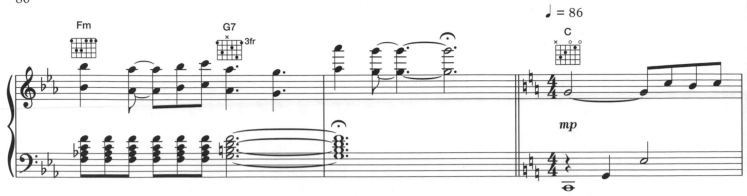

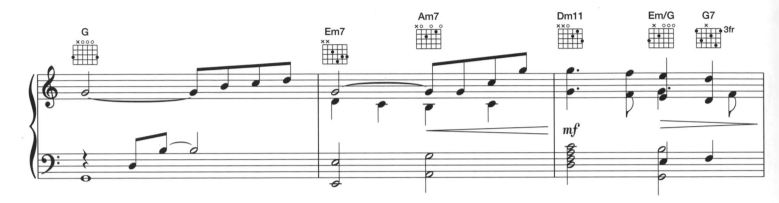

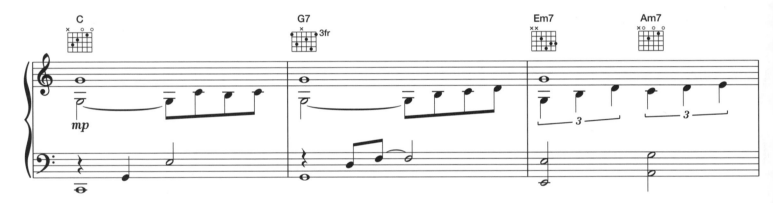

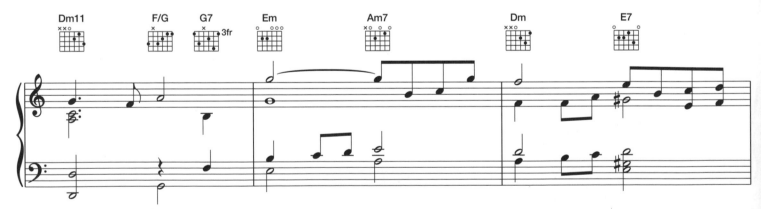

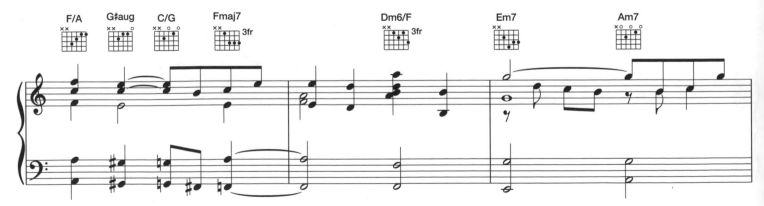

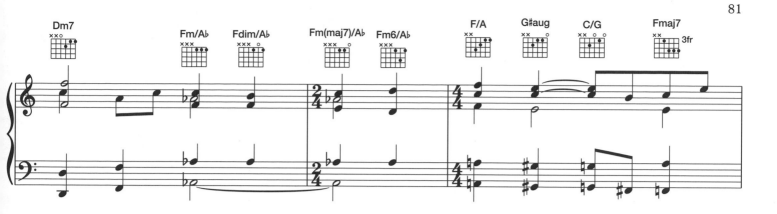

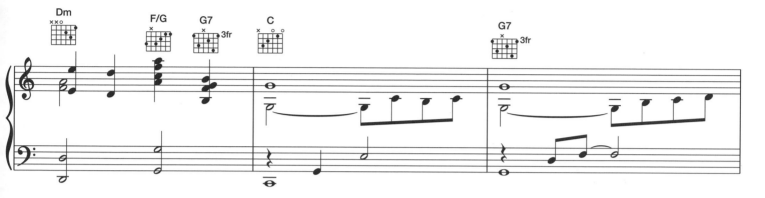

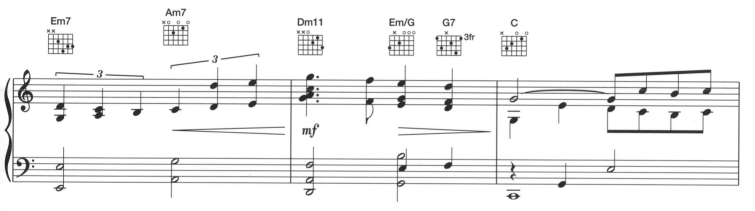

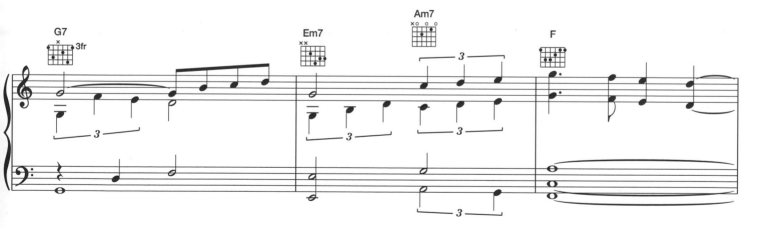

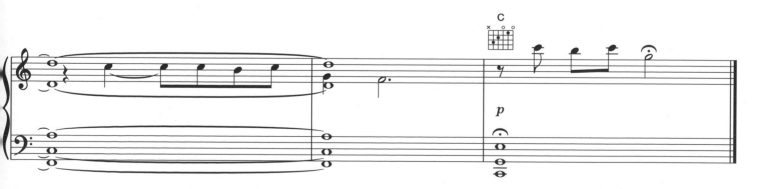

Pretender Got My Heart

Words and Music by James Hogarth,
Karen Poole, Michelle Poole and Terence Martin

And now all I have___ is what you for - got___ and it's all be-cause of you, babe.

And all that my heart___ needs now___ is a rest - ing place if___ it's not too

late. ___ ooh, ___ ooh, ___ ooh. ___ (Pre-tend-er)

Ooh, ooh, ooh, ooh,___

Ooh, ooh, ooh, ooh,_ ooh, ___ ooh, ___ ooh.

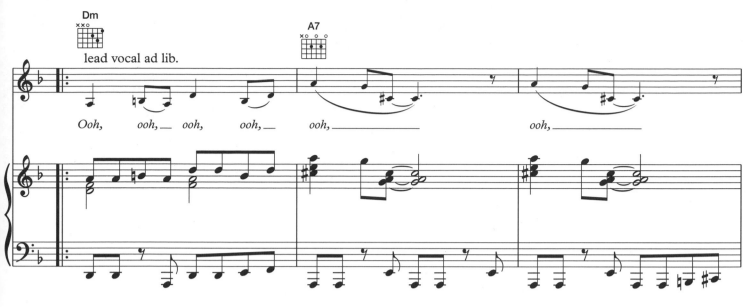

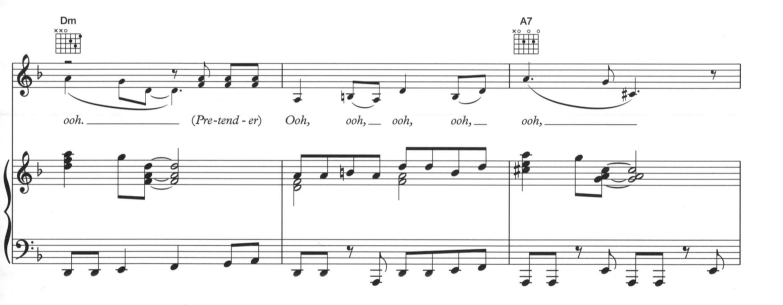

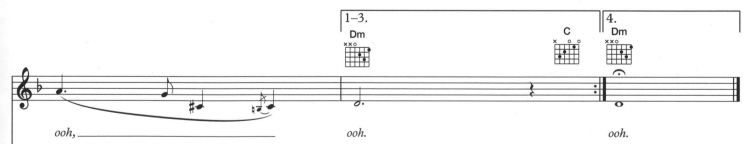

Ring, Ring, Ring

Words and Music by Aaron Soul,
Anthony Briscoe and Mohammed Jeilan

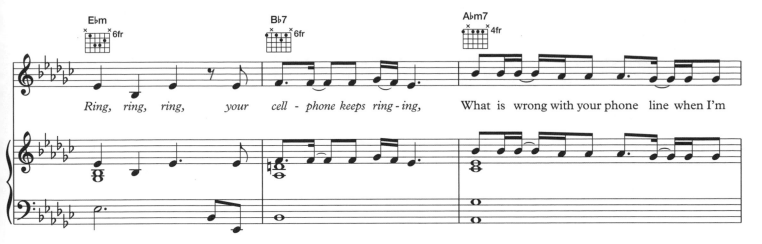

Ring, ring, ring, your cell - phone keeps ring - ing, What is wrong with your phone line when I'm

ring-ing to see __ if you're feel - ing fine? Ring, ring, ring, my cell - phone's not ring - ing,

Now you got __ me won-der-ing, now you got __ me pa - nick-ing. Ring, ring, ring, your

cell - phone keeps ring - ing, girl, you got __ me think-ing 'bout the things I would say __ yeah. __

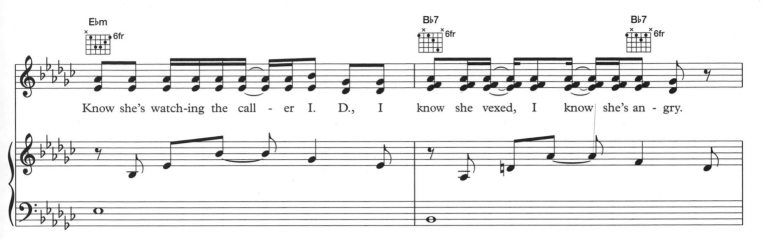

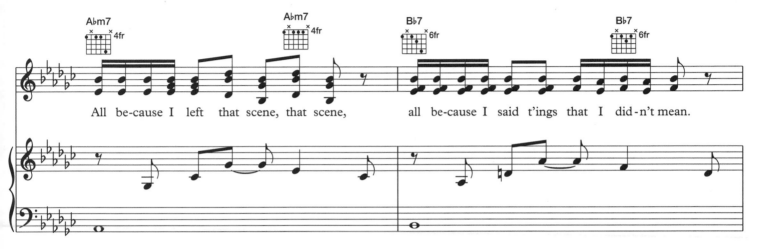

should tell__ her she__ should watch her__ back, 'cause__ I

might find__ a - no - ther__ to scratch my__ back. But__ in

the mean - time__ I__ am still wait - ing__ for__ my

D.%. al Fine

phone to__ start sing - ing__ and ring, ring,__ ring, ring, ring,__ ring.

Woman Trouble

Words and Music by Robbie Craig,
Mark Hill, Pete Devreaux and Craig David

ble,___ wo - man_ trou - ble,___ wo - man__ trou - ble,___ wo - man_ trou -

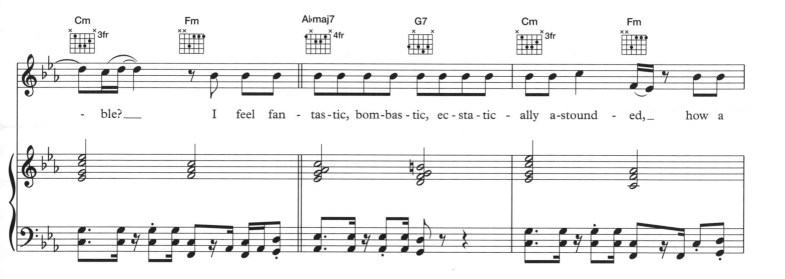

- ble?___ I feel fan - tas -tic, bom-bas -tic, ec -sta -tic - ally a-stound - ed,_ how a

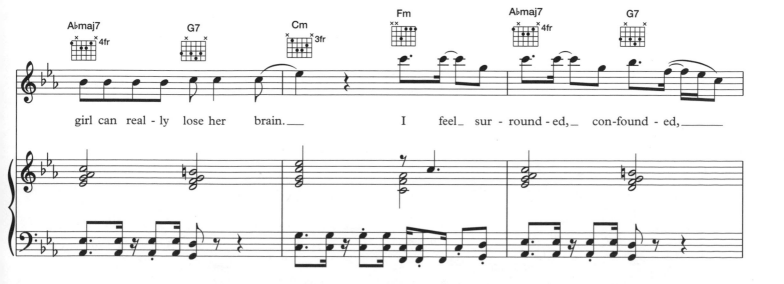

girl can real - ly lose her brain.___ I feel_ sur -round -ed,_ con-found -ed,_____

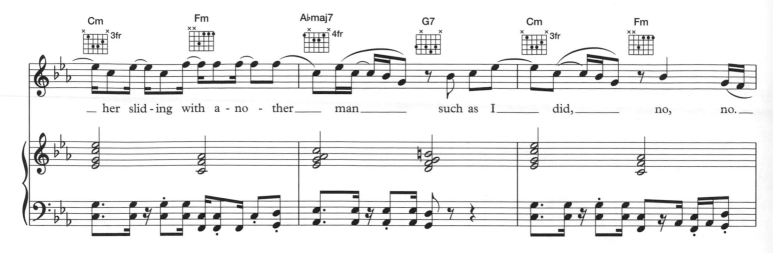

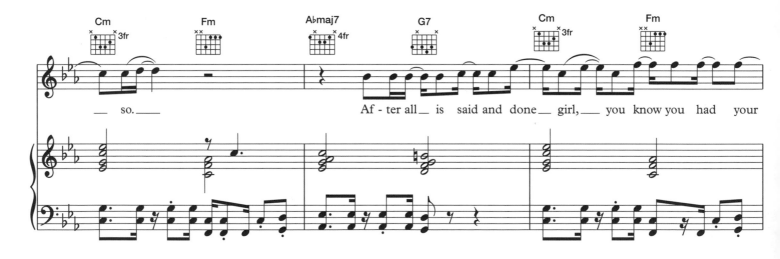

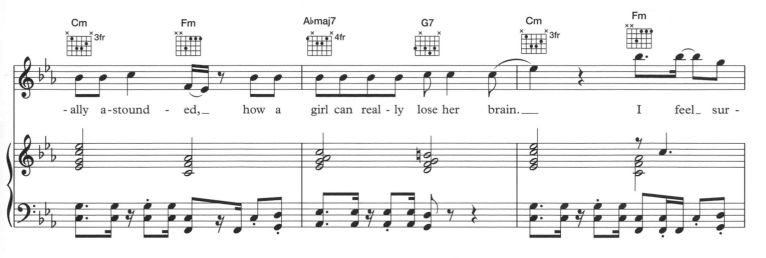

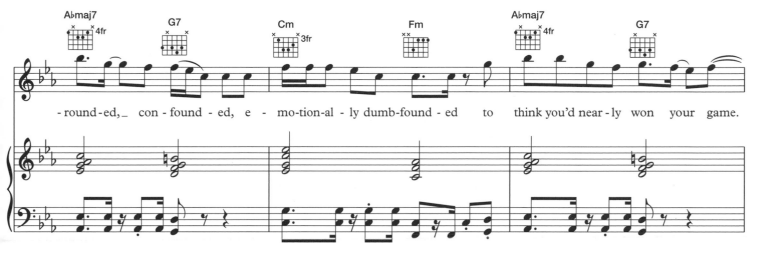

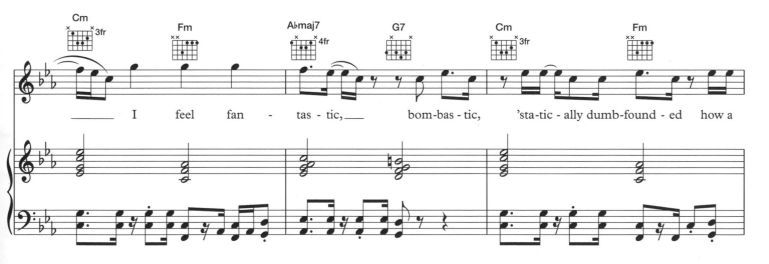

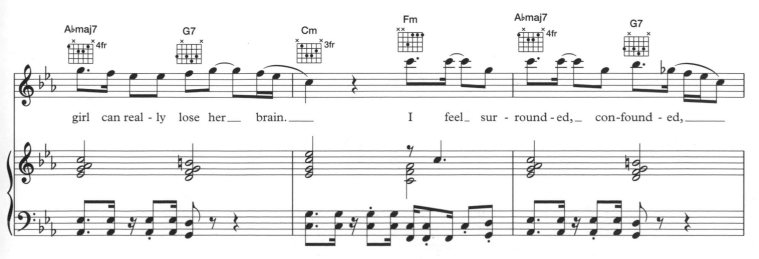

'mo-tion-ally dumb-found-ed, to think you've near-ly won__ your game,_____ oh__ yeah.

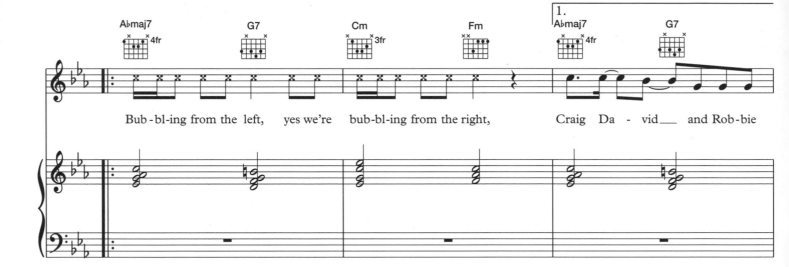

Bub-bl-ing from the left, yes we're bub-bl-ing from the right, Craig Da - vid__ and Rob-bie

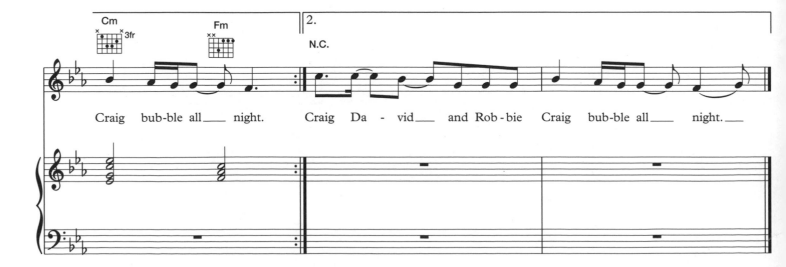

Craig bub-ble all__ night. Craig Da - vid__ and Rob-bie Craig bub-ble all__ night.__